Parrots

The illustrated identifier to over 70 species

Parrots

The illustrated identifier to over 70 species

Dr Sharmila Choudhury and Adam White

APPLE

A QUINTET BOOK

Published by the Apple Press
6 Blundell Street
London N7 9BH

ISBN 1-85076-788-2

This book was designed and produced by
Quintet Publishing Limited
6 Blundell Street
London N7 9BH

Creative Director: Richard Dewing
Art Director: Clare Reynolds
Designer: Rita Wüthrich
Senior Project Editor: Sally Green
Editor: Deborah Gray
Photography: Cyril Laubscher

Typeset in Great Britain by
Central Southern Typesetters, Eastbourne
Manufactured in Singapore
by Bright Arts Pte Ltd
Printed in Singapore
by Star Standard Industries Pte Ltd

Contents

All of the photographs in this book were taken
by Cyril Laubscher, Natural History Photographer,
44 Moyser Drive, Orpington, Kent BR5 4PW England

Introduction

What is a Parrot?

Parrots are birds belonging to the family *Psittacidae*, the only family in the order Psittaciformes. They are colorful, mainly tropical birds with a very distinctive down-curved hooked bill, which they use to feed on fruits, seeds, and nectar. Another distinguishing feature of parrots is their scaly legs and feet which have two toes pointing forward and two pointing backwards. In addition, all parrots have a fleshy often colorful cere, which attaches the base of the upper mandible to the skull.

The Parrots consist of three distinct subgroups: the Lories and Lorikeets, which feed on pollen and nectar using long brush-tipped tongues; the Cockatoos, which have erectable crests on their heads, and short, stubby tongues; and the typical Parrots and Parakeets, which have broad fleshy tongues complete with spoon-shaped tips.

Parrot Size and Color

Parrots come in all shapes and sizes, from the tiny Buff-faced Pygmy Parrot which only just attains 3¼in (8cm) in length, to the large Hyacinth Macaw which is 39in (1m) long. In general the male is slightly larger than the female, although in some lovebirds the opposite is true.

Parrots are extremely colorful birds, often sporting brilliant greens, yellows, and reds. Both sexes are generally similar in plumage. An extreme exception is the Eclectus Parrot, in which the male is green, while the female is a brilliant red. Some parrots have erectable crests on their heads, others have long feathers that trail from their necks.

Right: Galahs (Eolophus roseicepillus) were originally found in the arid scrubland of Australia. They are one of the few species which have adapted to the changing environment and can now be found on cultivated land, parkland, and even in some suburbs.

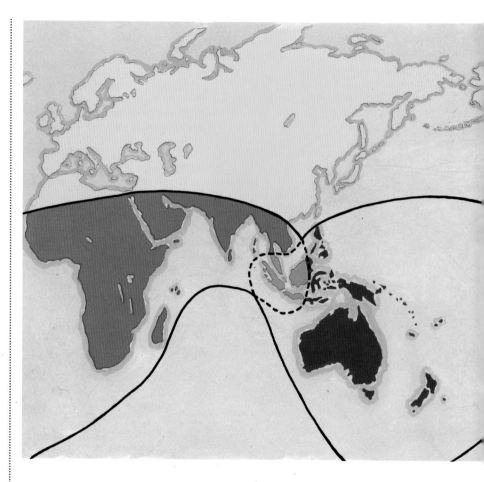

Parrot Distribution

There are over 360 species of parrots and most of them are found in tropical regions of the Southern Hemisphere, i.e. South and Central America, the Caribbean Islands, Africa, Australasia, and the Pacific Islands. Some parrots are also found in temperate zones, with the northernmost bird being the Slaty-headed Parakeet in Afghanistan, and the southernmost being the Austral Conure which lives in southern Chile.

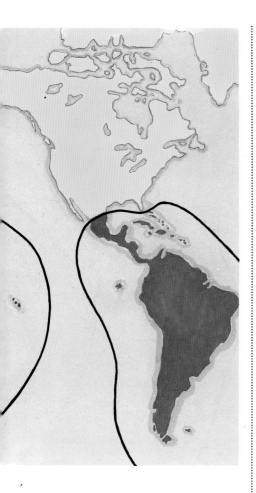

Broadly, parrots can be split into three regional groups: South American, Afro-Asian, and the Pacific Parrots.

Parrot Habitat

Parrots are found mainly in lowland tropical rainforests. They tend to be non-migratory, staying all year round in their local patch of forest where they can find enough food at all times of the year. However, there are some parrots which live in arid regions, such as the Budgerigar and the Cockatiel, these lead a nomadic existence, always following the rains. Some parrots living on islands also migrate to other islands or the mainland, but these distances are generally short.

Most parrots live high up in trees where they feed on the fruits, flowers, and seeds of that tree, but there are exceptions. Three species do in fact live on the ground. Those are the Kakapo of New Zealand, the Ground Parrot, and the Night Parrot of Australia. In addition, some parrots have conquered mountainous regions, for instance the New Zealand Kea or the Derbyan Parakeet in Tibet, while there are others that live on the sea shore. Among their number are the Rock Parakeet and the Red-fronted Parakeet.

Parrot Food

Parrots are mostly vegetarians, feeding on a variety of fruits, seeds, flowers, nectar, pollen, tubers, and roots. Their powerful beaks and thick tongues are particularly adapted for cracking and de-husking hard seeds, while their feet are often used with great skill as "hands" in holding the food. The Lories and Lorikeets are specialized for feeding on pollen and nectar, which they pick up with their brush-tipped tongues. Black Cockatoos from Australia also regularly feed on insect larvae.

As this Blue-and-Yellow Macaw (Ara araruana) demonstrates, many parrots can grasp and manipulate objects with a dexterity rivaling some of the primates. They have highly moveable and very powerful bills, a thick fleshy tongue, and feet with grasping pairs of opposing toes.

Parrot Breeding Biology

Most parrots are monogamous and many stay paired to the same partner for life. Since some parrots may live to be up to 50 years old, this is indeed a long time. The courtship displays of parrots tend to be quite simple, at the most involving bowing, spreading of the wings, raising of the feet, and dilating pupils. The Palm Cockatoo, however, has a spectacular territorial display – pirouetting on the top of a dead trunk, beating the trunk with a stick held in his foot. Pair bonds are maintained by mutual preening and courtship feeding. Exceptions to this are two New Zealand parrots, the Kea, which is polygamous, and the Kakapo, a lekking species, the males of which gather to perform courtship rituals.

Newly hatched parrots bear little resemblance to their parents apart from the relatively massive head and powerful bill. Although it will fledge in nearly two months, it will take four years before this five week old Red-tailed Black Cockatoo (Calyptorhynchus banksii) reaches sexual maturity.

In general, very little is known about the breeding biology of parrots as most of the information comes from birds in captivity. Parrots generally start breeding at the age of three to four years. They typically nest in holes within trees, either using natural cavities or those made by other animals. However, some parrots use other nest sites: the Rock Parakeet and Patagonion Conure nest in cliffs; the Pygmy Parrots, the Golden-shouldered Parrot, and the Red-faced Lovebird nest within termite mounds; while the Monk Parakeets build huge colonial nests out of twigs.

Parrots lay between one and eight eggs which they incubate for 17–35 days before the chicks hatch. Generally the female alone incubates the eggs, only in the Cockatoo family does the male share this duty. The tiny naked pink chicks are fed for 21–70 days in the nest by both parents until they have grown their feathers and are large enough to survive the outside world. After they leave the nest the young are often still fed by the parents for a brief time before they can finally fend for themselves.

Parrot Calls

Parrots are not known as great songsters among birds, but they do have a remarkable vocal repertoire. Their calls are generally simple whistles or harsh metallic notes, any variation achieved by the repetition of the notes. Parrots also have the ability to mimic sounds. Captive African Gray Parrots (*Psittacus erithacus*) are capable of mimicking an astonishing vocabulary; record holding birds have recited over 800 words.

Parrot Intelligence

Parrots are amongst the most intelligent of birds and indeed one of the most intelligent of all groups of animals. They are highly sociable birds, generally living in large groups or flocks. Their societies are complex and they show various forms of play behavior, courtship and ritualized fighting.

Parrot Conservation

From early times, parrots have been valued by man both for their feathers and as pets. In recent years, however, the pet trade has become a highly lucrative multi-million dollar business, and the extensive trade, with parrots caught directly from the wild, has endangered the survival of many species. In addition, the native habitat of many parrots is increasingly being destroyed. The tropical rainforests are felled for their timber and to make clearance for agriculture.

The St Vincent Amazon (Amazona guildingii) is one of 78 species of parrots currently facing threats against their survival. Although their capture for the pet trade has been controlled, their restricted range on the island of St. Vincent in the Caribbean makes them vulnerable to habitat destruction and hurricanes.

Parrots as Pets

Parrots are extremely popular pets because of their lovely colors, their playful behavior, and their ability to mimic sounds, including the human voice. The most commonly kept parrot is the Budgerigar, bred in all sorts of colors in captivity, but which in the wild is only found in green. Generally parrots are easy to keep and can be fed on a seed mixture supplemented with regular fruit and green food.

Selective breeding over many years has produced many "unnatural" variations of the Budgerigar (Melopsittacus undulatus). These are far removed from the huge nomadic swirling flocks of green and yellow birds encountered in the Australian outback.

HOW TO USE THIS BOOK

The species in this book are arranged into three main groups: *the Lories and Lorikeets, the Cockatoos,* and *the typical Parrots and Parakeets.* For most of these the sexes look similar, so only one bird is illustrated.

Key to Symbols
The main facts about each bird are encoded in simple at-a-glance symbols which fall into two main categories: region/continent and conservation status.
Not in danger means that populations are healthy and not under serious threat at the present time.

Vulnerable means that although currently not endangered, populations are relatively low and may become endangered if current threats continue.
Endangered means under serious threat of becoming extinct in the wild if action is not taken, and the current threats removed.

| **Afro-Asian** | **Pacific** | **Southern America** | **Not in danger** | **Vulnerable** | **Endangered** |

Lories and Lorikeets
(Subfamily Loriinae)

The Lories and Lorikeets are found in Australia, the Pacific Islands, New Guinea, and the adjacent islands. They are small- to medium-sized birds with extremely colorful and glossy plumage. They fly around in large, noisy flocks from one flowering tree to the next. Most of them are pollen and nectar specialists, dipping their long, brush-tipped tongues deep into the flowers to lick up the pollen and sugary nectar. Some also eat seeds and insects.

Black Lory ♦ *Chalcopsitta atra*

Description Length 13in (32cm). Weight 9oz (260g). Plumage is black with a purple gloss, only the rump a bright purple blue and the underside of the tail yellow and red. The bill is black and the eyes orange red. Sexes similar. In young birds the bare skin around the eyes and lower mandible are white instead of black.
Call A high chitter.
Distribution Western New Guinea and adjacent islands.
Habitat Mostly found in open habitats such as savannah grasslands, forest edges, coastal plantations, and mangrove swamps.
Food Nectar.
Breeding Lays 2 eggs which are brooded by both parents and hatch after 25 days.

Brown Lory ♦ Duivenbode's Lory ♦ *Chalcopsitta duivenbodei*

This bird is generally seen in pairs or in small flocks at flowering trees, but at night roosts socially in large flocks.

Description Length 12in (31cm). Weight 8oz (230g). Plumage is generally dark olive brown, but forehead, throat, and cheeks are yellow. The breast-feathers, neck, and bend of wing are streaked with yellow. Thighs and underside of wings are orange yellow, whilst the rump is violet blue. Males also have yellow markings on the outer tail feathers which females lack. The bill is black and eyes red.

Call Very loud, musical notes as well as hissing and screeching call.

Distribution Northern New Guinea.

Habitat Brown Lories inhabit lowland forests up to about 650ft (200m). They commonly feed on flowering trees.

Food Nectar.

Breeding Nests are built within cavities in the trunks of large forest trees. 2 eggs are laid and incubated for 24 days before the chicks hatch. The young leave the nest after about 11 weeks.

Yellow-Streaked Lory ♦ *Chalcopsitta sintillata*

A common bird, usually found in noisy flocks of up to thirty birds. Has a direct, flapping flight.

Description Length 12in (31cm). Weight 6½–8½oz (180–245g). Plumage generally dark green streaked with yellow. Bright red markings on forehead, thighs, underside of wings, and underside of tail. A black band stretches across the back of the head and ears. In flight a yellow band becomes visible across the underside of the flight feathers. Bill is black and eyes yellow to orange red. Females less red on forehead.

Call An occasional squeak or squeal whilst feeding, in flight a shrill screech.

Distribution Southern New Guinea.

Habitat Live in lowland savannahs and nearby forests.

Food They feed on nectar from the flowers of umbrella trees.

Breeding Nests are built in hollow tree cavities. 2 eggs are laid and incubated for 24 days. The young leave the nest after 11–13 weeks.

Violet-Necked Lory ♦ *Eos squamata*

Usually found in pairs or small flocks of up to ten birds.
Description Length 10½in (27cm). Weight 4oz (110g). Plumage is highly variable, but generally red and purple. A violet-blue collar around the neck may be broad in some birds and almost lacking in others. Belly is purple, and tail is purple above and brown red below. Wing feathers are tipped with purple and black. Bill is orange and eyes yellow to red.
Call Shrill screech.

Distribution Found in Indonesia, and West Papuan Islands.
Habitat Primary mountain forest up to 3,300ft (1,000m), but also inhabit secondary forests, mangroves, and coconut plantations.
Food Nectar.
Breeding 2 eggs laid and incubated by female for 27 days. Young leave nest after 9 weeks.

Blue-Streaked Lory ♦ *Eos reticulata*

This used to be a very common lowland species, but the population has suffered due to mass trapping and deforestation.
Description Length 12in (31cm). Weight 5½oz (160g). General plumage bright red streaked with purple blue. A blue band stretches from the eye down to the neck. The back is streaked with violet and blue, and the wing feathers are tipped with black. Tail is brownish black above and dull red below. Bill coral color, eyes orange red. Sexes similar.

Call Shrill screech and high-pitched whistle.
Distribution Indonesia.
Habitat Inhabit coastal mangroves, forests, and plantations.
Food Unknown.
Breeding 2 eggs are laid and incubated for 25 days. The young birds leave the nest about 12 weeks after hatching.

Red Lory (Moluccan Lory) ♦ *Eos Bornea*

A noisy and conspicuous parrot, usually in large flocks of up to thirty.
Description Length 12in (31cm). Weight 6oz (170g). General plumage bright red. The wing feathers are tipped with black; the tail is reddish brown above and dull red below. Bill is orange and eyes are red. Sexes similar.
Call Shrill, two-syllable screech.
Distribution Indonesia.
Habitat Very common in plantations, near human settlements, in coastal forests, and mangroves. They feed on flowering or fruiting trees, flying from tree to tree in large flocks.
Food Fruit, nectar.
Breeding Nests are built in hollows high up in old trees. 2 eggs are laid and incubated for 24 days. The young are ready to leave the nest after 9–10 weeks.

Rainbow Lorikeet ♦ Swainson's Lorikeet ♦ *Trichoglossus haematodus*

Very common, generally seen in pairs or flocks of up to a few hundred birds. They are noisy and active birds, circling above the tree-tops with loud screeches or clambering about in the foliage with chattering notes.

Description Length 10in (26cm). Weight 3½–5½oz (100–155g). Plumage rainbow-colored. The head bluish mauve with a yellow collar around back of neck. Back and wings are green. Breast is red with blue black bars, belly dark green, and thighs yellow green. Tail green above, dull yellow below. In flight a broad, yellow band stretches across underside of flight feathers. Bill and eyes are red.

Call Shrill chattering while feeding, and a sharp screech repeated at intervals in flight.

Distribution Found in Indonesia, New Guinea and islands off the east coast, Australia, Tasmania.

Habitat Though more common in the lowlands, also found as high as 7,200ft (2,200m). Virtually all types of wooded country, including rainforests, casuarina groves, coconut plantations, gardens, and parks. They are highly nomadic, moving around in search of flowering trees.

Food Pollen, nectar, fruits, berries, seeds, leaf buds, insects, and their larvae. They commonly feed on pollen and nectar from blossoming eucalyptus, melaleuca and banksia trees. They also often raid orchards and cereal plantations, feeding on apples, pears, maize, and sorghum.

Breeding Nests are built in a hollow tree trunk or branch. 2 eggs are laid and incubated by the female alone for 25 days. Both parents feed the chicks which leave the nest 7–8 weeks after hatching.

Dusky Lory ♦ *Pseudeos fuscata*

Nomadic birds that follow the flush of flowering trees often crossing high mountain chains during their seasonal migrations. Highly sociable birds, usually in flocks of 20–100 birds. Dusky Lories are often quite tame and approachable.
Description Length 10in (25cm). Weight 5–7oz (135–190g). Plumage highly variable, generally a dusky, olive brown with orange red and yellow markings. Crown dull yellow, a band of yellow around neck, sometimes a second band across breast. Lower breast and thighs yellow to orange red. Rump is a creamy white, tail a dull, olive yellow. Bill orange, eyes red.
Call Shrill high-pitched screech.
Distribution New Guinea.

Habitat Mainly found in hills and mountains up to 7,900ft (2,400m). Locally common to abundant in forests, groves of flowering trees, parks, and gardens. Also sometimes found in savannah, coconut, and teak plantations. Dusky lories feed in flowering or fruiting trees.
Food Fruit, nectar.
Breeding Nests built in holes high up in forest trees. 2 eggs are laid which the female incubates. Eggs hatch after about 24 days and young leave the nest after 10 weeks.

Yellow-and-Green Lorikeet ♦ *Trichoglossus flavoviridis*

A shy bird, tending to stay in dense foliage where its plumage blends with the leaves. When disturbed, flies off screeching loudly.
Description Length 8in (21cm). Weight 2oz (50g). The general plumage is green and yellow, with head and breast yellow barred with green. Back, wings, and tail are green above, the tail is yellow below. The bill and eyes are orange.
Call A pleasant warble.
Distribution Sulawesi and Sula Islands, Indonesia.
Habitat This is a true forest bird, occurring from lowlands to upper mountain forests and feeding in flowering trees. Common and widespread, it is usually seen in small noisy flocks.
Food Fruit and nectar.

Breeding Lays 2 eggs, which are then incubated for about 23 days. The young leave about 65 days after hatching.

Goldie's Lorikeet ♦ *Trichoglossus goldiei*

They are highly sociable birds, usually found in large flocks which keep in contact with a distinctive loud call.
Description Length 7½in (19cm). Weight 1½–2oz (45–55g). General plumage green, with more yellow on underparts. The head is a dark red, duller and less extensive in females, with a dark blue patch around the eyes. Tail is

green above, yellowish below. In flight, a yellow band stretches across underside of flight feathers. Bill is black and eyes are brown.
Call Single loud hiss.
Distribution New Guinea.
Habitat Mostly found in primary forest and flowering trees at mid-mountain heights. They are highly nomadic, following flowering trees up and down the mountain side. Wherever there are flowering trees, they can become locally very abundant.
Food Fruit, berries, nectar, pollen, and flowers. They are particularly fond of those from eucalyptus and grevillea trees.
Breeding 2 eggs are laid. Little else is known about their breeding biology.

Chattering Lory ♦ *Lorius garrulus*

These parrots are good "talkers" and hence extremely popular as pets. In the wild they are noisy and conspicuous birds, flying from tree to tree with loud screeching calls. They usually occur in pairs.

Description Length 12in (30cm). Weight 7oz (200g). General plumage red and green. Head, breast and abdomen are a bright red, whilst the wings, back, and thighs are dark green. The bend of the wings is yellow. The bill is orange, the eyes yellow to orange red.

Call A low gurgling when feeding, but a loud screeching or braying call in flight.

Distribution Found in Moluccan Islands and Indonesia.

Habitat Mainly a coastal bird, but also found in primary and secondary forests and in coconut plantations. Used to be a very common bird, but local trade and the clearing of forests appears to be causing a decline in numbers.

Food Fruit, nectar.

Breeding Nest in tree holes, sometimes high up in the canopy. 2 eggs are laid and brooded by the female for 26 days. The young leave the nest about 10–11 weeks after hatching.

Black-Capped Lory ♦ *Lorius lory*

A locally common but shy parrot that rarely allows a close approach. They usually fly around in pairs or trios. Larger flocks may come together to feed on flowering or fruiting trees.

Description Length 12½in (31cm). Weight 7–9oz (200–260g). General plumage red and blue black. The crown and back of the neck are black; the breast, abdomen, and thighs are a dark metallic blue. The face and front of the neck are bright red; the wings are bronze green. The tail is red above, tipped with blue black, and olive yellow below. In flight, a broad yellow band stretches across the underside of the flight feathers. The bill and eyes are orange and the flesh around the bill is gray.

Call A loud ringing cry.

Distribution New Guinea, Western Papuan islands.

Habitat Found in the upper storys of forest trees, mainly in the lowlands, but sometimes up to 5,250ft (1,600m).

Food Fruit, nectar, pollen, flowers, insects, and their larvae. Possibly also seeds.

Breeding The courtship display of the male consists of a bobbing up and down with the whole body, wings fully spread. Two eggs are laid and incubated by the female for about 24 days. The young leave the nest about 9–10 weeks after hatching.

Musk Lorikeet ◆ *Glossopsitta concinna*

These are extremely noisy birds, their continuous screeching always giving away their presence in the trees despite their camouflaged plumage. In flight, their fast and "whirring" wing beats can be clearly heard.
Description Length 8½in (22cm). Weight 2oz (50–60g). General plumage bright green. Underparts slightly more yellowish green with yellow patches on the sides of the breast. A red band stretches from the forehead across the sides of the head. Crown is a bright blue. The back of the neck is bronze. The bill is black tipped with orange and the eyes are orange. Sexes are similar.
Call Shrill screech and a low chattering.
Distribution South-eastern Australia and Tasmania.

Habitat Occur at low altitudes and prefer open habitats, but will be found wherever there are flowering or fruiting trees. They follow the blossom, traveling around in small flocks and can often be seen climbing among the branches of flowering eucalyptus. They sometimes become pests in orchards and also raid maize fields.
Food Nectar, pollen, flowers, fruits, berries, seeds, and insects. They are particularly fond of the blossoms of eucalyptus trees.
Breeding Nests are built in hollow tree trunks or branches, usually high up in a eucalyptus near water. 2 eggs are laid and incubated by the female for about 22–30 days. The young leave the nest about 7 weeks after hatching.

Red-Flanked Lorikeet ♦ Pleasing Lorikeet ♦ *Charmosyna placentis*

Although common in the wild, this lorikeet is easily overlooked because of its small size and green plumage. They generally occur in small flocks in the canopy of flowering trees.
Description Length 6½in (17cm). Weight 1½oz (40g). General plumage green with yellower underparts. Males have a yellowish crown, blue ear coverts and rump. The cheek patches and flanks are red. The tail is green tipped with red and yellow; and a yellow band stretches across the underside of the flight feathers. Bill and legs are red, the eyes yellow orange. Females have a green crown, no red, and ear coverts are streaked yellow and black.

Call Shrill chattering and screech.
Distribution Indonesia, New Guinea, Western Papuan islands through to the Nuguria Islands.
Habitat Widespread and common in lowland forests, savannah woodlands, and coastal plantations.
Food Nectar, pollen, flowers.
Breeding The birds excavate a nesting hole either in termite mounds, in the bases of staghorn ferns, or in trees. 2 eggs are laid and incubated by both male and female for about 23 days. The young are ready to leave the nest after about 7 weeks.

Josephine's Lorikeet ♦ *Charmosyna josefinae*

These are quiet and unobtrusive birds. They fly silently through the trees either in pairs or small groups, only occasionally uttering a soft squeak.

Description Length 9½in (24cm). Weight 2½oz (70g). General plumage red and green. Head, neck, breast, and back are red. The mantle and wings are dark green. The back of the head, the thighs, and lower abdomen are black. The rump has a dusky blue patch. The tail is red tipped with yellow. Bill and legs are orange, the eyes are yellow. In females the back is green instead of red.

Call They make a nasal *eng* when perched and a high-pitched screech in flight.

Distribution New Guinea.

Habitat Mainly at mid-mountain heights in forests, forest edges, and partially cleared land.

Food Pollen, nectar, flowers, and possibly soft fruits.

Breeding 2 eggs are laid and incubated by both male and female for 25 days. The young leave the nest after 8 weeks.

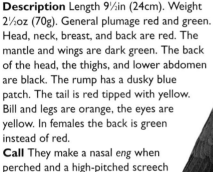

Musschenbroek's Lorikeet ♦ Yellow-billed Lorikeet ♦
Neopsittacus musschenbroekii

A mountain forest bird that is more usually seen either in pairs or small flocks in the company of other lorikeets, running along the stout branches in the upper and middle storys of trees.

Description Length 9in (23cm). Weight 2oz (50g). General plumage green and red. Head and neck are olive brown streaked with yellow. Wings and back are dark green, underparts are yellow green with a bright red breast and center of abdomen. Tail is green tipped with yellow, and in flight a broad red band stretches across the underside of the flight feathers. Bill is yellow, eyes are red, legs gray.

Call A descending musical trill or screech consisting of two or three syllables. In flight a short staccato screech.

Distribution New Guinea.

Habitat Widespread in forests between 5,250–9,200ft (1,600–2,800m). This Lorikeet is one of the few mountain forest birds that has actually benefited from human activities, being particularly common in partly cleared forests, and around village gardens and roads.

Food Nectar, pollen, flowers, fruits, berries, seeds, and possibly insects too.

Breeding Nests are built in the holes of tall trees, where 2 eggs are laid. Incubation is for 23 days and the young then stay in the nest for 8 weeks.

Papuan Lorikeet ♦ *Charmosyna papou*

These birds move about in a peculiar jerky manner, flicking their long tails. Their brilliant colors make them conspicuous in flight, but they are easily overlooked when feeding amongst flowering trees.

Description Length 16½in (42cm). Weight 3½oz (95g). General plumage red and dark green. Head, neck, breast, and lower abdomen red, only the crown has a black patch streaked with blue. Mantle and wings are dark green. A broad black band stretches across the abdomen and thighs, and a thin one across the back of the neck. Yellow patches on flanks and sides of breast. The rump is blue and the tail green tipped with yellow. Bill and legs are orange, eyes are yellow.

Call Both a soft *cheep-cheep* and a surprisingly mellow screech.

Distribution New Guinea.

Habitat Mountain forests between 4,900–11,500ft (1,500–3,500m). Usually seen in pairs or small groups, hopping amongst the moss-covered branches and blossoms of flowering trees.

Food Nectar, pollen, flowers, fruits, berries, seeds, and probably insects.

Breeding 2 eggs are laid and incubated by both male and female for 26 days or more. The young remain in the nest for about 8 weeks.

Cockatoos
(Subfamily Cacatuinae)

The Cockatoos are found in Australia, New Guinea, and the islands that are adjacent to the Philippines. They are large birds with an erectable crest and their plumage is generally white, pink, gray, or black, with various red or yellow markings. They have a short bill and short, stubby tongue, which they use to crack open seeds and nuts.

White-Tailed Black Cockatoo ♦ *Calyptorhynchus funereus*

These are noisy and conspicuous birds, usually found in family parties or small groups. They are wary and difficult to approach, one or two birds always acting as sentinels and giving a screeching alarm call to warn of danger, when the entire group flies off.

Description Length 26in (67cm). Weight 1½–2lb (750–900g). General plumage brownish black, but feathers are margined with white. The ear coverts and the outer tail are white. Females have brighter white ear coverts and a much more heavily spotted tail.

In males the bill is dark gray, in females horn-colored. The eyes are brown but have a ring of naked flesh around them, pink in males and gray in females.

Call A prolonged screaming *kee-ow* in flight. When feeding a peculiar grating note.

Distribution South-west Australia.

Habitat Found mainly in heavily forested areas. Occasionally large flocks come to feed in pine plantations or on freshly burnt land to extract the seeds from banksia cones split open by the fire.

Food They feed mainly on seeds, nuts, berries, blossoms, wood-boring larvae, and beetles. Particularly fond of seeds of eucalyptus, acacia, hakea, banksia and pinus.

Breeding The male displays by raising his short crest, spreading his tail to show the tail band and bowing to the female. The nest is usually built in a spacious hollow of a eucalyptus tree, and 1–2 eggs are laid. The female alone incubates the egg for 29 days. The chick remains in the nest for a further 12–13 weeks, at first only fed by the female, and later by the male as well.

Palm Cockatoo ♦ *Probosciger aterrimus*

This large and distinguished-looking bird is amongst the most impressive of all parrots. Unfortunately, despite being legally protected they are still hunted for food and for the live-bird trade by local people and have become quite rare.

Description Length 2ft (60cm). Weight 2–2¼lb (0.9–1kg). Entire plumage is almost a uniform grayish black with only the forehead being black and the naked cheek patches a crimson red. Long erectable crest feathers. The bill and legs are gray black and the eyes brown. The female differs by having a much shorter beak.

Call A deep mellow note followed by a drawn-out high note which ends abruptly with an upward inflection. There is also a mournful, wailing cry, a deep whistle repeated 3–4 times, and a sharp, guttural screech when alarmed.

Distribution New Guinea, Indonesia, Northern Australia.

Habitat Found in rainforests, partially cleared areas, secondary forest, monsoon woodland, and dense savannah, mainly in the lowlands and foothills. They usually occur in pairs or small groups, perched high up on the branches of tall trees or flying above the canopy.

Food Fruits, seeds, nuts, and leaf buds.

Breeding Male has a spectacular territorial display where he slowly pirouettes on the top of a dead trunk with wings outspread and crest raised, beating the trunk with a stout stick in his foot. The nest is built in the hollow of a tree trunk or branch. A single egg is laid and incubated by the female alone for about 30 days. The chick stays in the nest for another 7–8 weeks.

Red-Tailed Black Cockatoo ◆ *Calyptorhynchus magnificus*

Noisy and conspicuous, often in large flocks.
Description Length 2ft (60cm).Weight
26oz (750g). Males are almost completely
black with a red band across the tail. Bill and
legs are dark gray, eyes brown. Females are
brownish-black spotted with yellow. The

tail-band is yellow to orange and crossed by
black bars.
Call A loud and metallic *kree* or *krurr* in
flight. Alarm call a sharp *kru-rak*.
Distribution Australia.
Habitat Dry woodland or trees bordering
waterways, as well as eucalyptus forests, and
savannah woodland. They are nomadic birds,
moving with the availability of food.
Food Seeds and nuts, particularly those of
eucalyptus, acacia, casuarina, banksia, hakea,
as well as ficus fruits.
Breeding Nests are usually built in large
hollow eucalyptus trees. The female alone
broods a single egg for 30
days, The chick stays in the
nest for another 3 months
and is fed by both parents.

Gang-Gang Cockatoo ◆ *Callocephalon fimbriatum*

Very approachable in the wild.
Description Length 14in (35cm). Weight
10oz (280g). General plumage gray, feathers
edged with white giving a barred
appearance. The male has a bright red head
and crest, the female a gray head. In both
sexes the bill is horn-colored, eyes brown.
Call A rasping screech ending in an upward
inflection. A soft growl whilst feeding.
Distribution South-eastern Australia.
Habitat Wooded valleys and mountain
forests up to 6,550ft (2,000m). During
winter they move down to lower altitudes
and into open forests and gardens.
Food They feed on seeds, particularly of
eucalyptus and acacia, and also nuts, fruits,
and insects.

Breeding They breed from October to
January. The nest is built high up in a tree
trunk or branch. 2 eggs are laid and both
male and female incubate
for 25–30 days. Both
parents feed the chicks for
about 8 weeks.

Galah ♦ Roseate Cockatoo, Rose-breasted Cockatoo ♦
Eolophus roseicapillus

These attractive parrots have become a common sight both in agricultural fields and in urban parks and gardens. In some areas, however, they have become a pest to local farmers, eating their crops.

Description Length 14in (35cm). Weight 11–13oz (300–350g). General plumage rose-pink and gray. The face, neck and most of the underparts are pink. The upperparts, wings, rump, lower abdomen, and tail are various shades of gray. The forehead and crown are white, and so is the erectable crest. The bill is horn-colored, and there is a ring of dark red naked flesh around the eyes, which is brown in males and red in females.

Call In flight a shrill cry, when alarmed a series of sharp shrieks.

Distribution Australia.

Habitat Common and widespread in most open country below 4,000ft (1,200m). They are typically found in savannah woodlands, open grasslands, and in fields of cereal crops. Also common in urban areas, nesting in gardens and parks.

Food They commonly feed on the ground, often in large flocks of hundreds of birds, taking seeds, grains, roots, shoots, leaf buds, and insects.

Breeding The courtship display consists of the male weaving his head from side to side with crest raised and strutting towards the female with soft calls. The female then flies off darting through the trees and the male follows in a display flight. The nest is built in a hollow branch or tree trunk, usually eucalyptus. 2–5 eggs are laid and incubated by both male and female for 25 days. The young leave the nest after 8 weeks.

Leadbeater's Cockatoo ♦ Pink Cockatoo, Major Mitchell's Cockatoo ♦ *Cacatua leadbeaterii*

These cockatoos are generally scarce and shy birds and will rarely allow close approach. Usually found in small groups, often with Galahs or Little Corellas, they fly by alternating flapping and gliding.

Description Length 14in (35cm). Weight 11–14oz (300–400g). General plumage white and salmon-pink. The face, neck, and breast are pink. The upperparts, wings, tail, and lower abdomen are white. The large raised crest is scarlet tipped with white and a central band of yellow, which is broader in females. The bill is white and legs are gray. In males the eyes are brown and in females reddish-pink.

Call A quavering cry. When alarmed three or four harsh screeches.

Distribution Australia.

Habitat Grasslands, dry acacia scrubland, arid woodlands, trees along cereal fields, and waterways. Where there is permanent water, the birds stay resident; elsewhere they are nomadic, always on the search for water.

Food They feed both on the ground and in trees or shrubs, eating seeds, nuts, fruits, and roots. They are particularly fond of callitris and acacia seeds.

Breeding When displaying the male raises his crest, struts along a branch and bobs his head up and down as well as swishing it sideways in a figure-eight movement. The female may respond by raising her crest and bowing. Breeding takes place between August to December, and the nest is in a tree hollow. 2–4 eggs are laid and incubated for 25 days by both parents, the male usually sitting during the day, the female at night. The young leave the nest after 8 weeks but remain with the parents as a family group.

Typical Parrots and Parakeets
(Subfamily Psittacinae)

Most parrots belong to this large and very varied group. The parrots belonging to the subfamily *Psittacinae* have very few characteristics in common, except that they have no erectable crests and most of them have broad, fleshy tongues with spoon-shaped tips.

Budgerigar ♦ *Melopsittacus undulatus*

A small nomadic parrot which lives in large dense flocks. Very familiar in captivity.
Description Length 7in (18cm). Weight 1oz (28g). Wild birds look similar to the classic green cage variety. Underparts are green, and the upper parts are strongly barred with yellow and black. The forehead, and throat are unbarred, but have several blue or black spots on the lower throat, while the long tail is bluish. The pale gray bill is small and unnoticeable with a blue fleshy base. The eye is white and the legs are gray-blue. Immatures are duller and have barring on the forehead.
Call Incessant chatter heard during flight, feeding, and resting.
Distribution Australia and feral populations in USA.
Habitat Budgerigars inhabit drier woodland, shrubland, and grassland.
Food They feed almost entirely on grass seeds on the ground.

Breeding In the wild they are opportunistic breeders, nesting anytime after rains. 4–8 eggs are laid in any suitable hole or crevice. Dead trees are used by many pairs. Incubation lasts about 18 days and the young are ready to leave within 5 weeks of hatching. If conditions are favorable they will often have several broods in any season.

Double-eyed Fig Parrot ♦ *Cyclopsitta diophthalma*

This small green parrot living in the upper branches of tall forest trees is easily overlooked. In flight they are noisy, but when feeding they seldom call – their giveaway is the steady stream of discarded pieces of fruit falling to the ground.
Description Length 5½in (14cm). Weight 1½–2oz (40–55g). General plumage green, paler and more yellowish on the underparts. The forehead is red, bordered by yellow on the crown, and the cheeks are red bordered by a purple-blue band. There is also a blue patch in front of the eyes. The flanks are yellow, and the underside of the wings are yellow to orange red. The bill is gray with a black tip, and the eyes are brown. In females the cheek patch is buff, not red.
Call A penetrating *tseet* repeated 2 or 3 times in rapid succession. There is also a high-pitched screech and sharp chattering.
Distribution New Guinea, Indonesia, North-eastern Australia.

Habitat All types of forests, tall secondary growth and partly cleared land in mid-mountains up to about 5,250ft (1,600m). Also in cultivated land, parks, and gardens.
Food Mainly fruits, particularly figs, and on seeds, nectar, and insects.
Breeding The birds excavate a nesting hole in the rotten limb or trunk of a tree. 2 eggs are laid and incubated for 21 days by the female. Initially only the female feeds the chicks, but later the male joins in. The young leave the nest after about 7–8 weeks.

Kea ♦ *Nestor notabilis*

Keas are famous for their mischievous nature, boldness and playfulness, climbing onto cars and entering ski lodges. They are also extremely intelligent and inquisitive, providing endless entertainment to New Zealand tourists and locals. But they are also known to cause considerable damage to human property.

Description Length 19in (48cm). Weight 35oz (1000g). General plumage olive green, the feathers being margined with black. Only the rump is orange red. In flight displays a bright flash of orange red on underside of wings, bordered by the orange yellow underside of the flight feathers. The bill is dark gray, and tends to be longer and more decurved in the male than in the female.

Call A range of soft, conversational notes and a harsh raucous *kee-aah* in flight.

Distribution New Zealand.

Habitat Fairly common in mountains between 2,000–6,550ft (600–2,000m), living in wooded valleys and nothofagus forests on the edge of sub-alpine scrublands. In spring and autumn they migrate up into the alpine scrub and grasslands to feed on seasonal fruits. In winter, heavy snowfall may force the birds to move below the timberline.

Food Almost anything from seeds, fruits, insects to scavenging on carcasses.

Breeding The nests are built deep inside crevices under rocks or roots of a tree, or in a hollow log on the ground. 3–4 eggs are laid and incubated by the female only for 28 days. The female feeds the chicks on her own for the first month, but then the male joins in and eventually takes over. The young leave the nest after 10–13 weeks.

Great-billed Parrot ♦ *Tanygnathus megalorynchos*

This parrot has a very large, heavy red bill giving it a top-heavy appearance. It uses this huge tool to crack open fruits and nuts.
Description Length 16in (41cm). Weight 9oz (260g). General plumage green. The top of the wings are black edged with yellow and then going over to green and blue edged with yellow. The rump is bright blue. The sides of the breast and undersides of the wing and flight feathers are yellow. The tail is short and round, tipped with yellow. The heavy bill is red in color and larger in males.

Call A loud quivering *squawk-squawk*.
Distribution Indonesia, islands around Sulawesi, Moluccan Islands, western Papuan, Tanimbar, Lesser Sunda Islands.
Habitat The Great-billed Parrot is an island bird, mainly found in the coastal lowlands and adjacent foothills, in primary forest, mangroves, and coastal plantations. It is widespread, but never encountered in large numbers. It prefers small islands, often traveling between them.
Food These parrots feed mainly on fruits and nuts, but they also raid corn crops. They are particularly fond of the large green fruits of *Sonneratia alba*, which grows on the beach.
Breeding Nests are built in holes high up in tall trees. 2 eggs are laid and incubated for 28 days. The young stay in the nest for about 9 weeks.

Red-winged Parrot ♦ Crimson-winged Parakeet ♦
Aprosmictus erythropterus

Shy and difficult to approach, and only occur in small flocks.

Description Length 12½in (32cm). Weight 4–5oz (120–150g). General plumage green. Wings red and black, bright blue rump. Underparts yellowish green, tail green tipped with yellow. Bill coral, eyes red. The female is duller green with a smaller area of red and no black on wings.

Call A soft chattering, screeches when alarmed. In flight a *crillik-crillik*.

Distribution Australia, New Guinea.

Habitat Open eucalyptus forests, melaleuca woodlands, acacia scrublands, casuarina and callitris groves, savannah woodlands, mangrove forests, any trees along waterways. They avoid dense forests.

Food They feed on fruits, seeds, nuts, flowers, nectar, and insects.

Breeding After making short flights around the female, the male perches on a branch and droops his wings, exposing the blue rump, and struts toward her. The nest is built in a very deep hollow in a tree, the egg chamber near ground level. 3–6 eggs are laid and incubated for 21 days by the female. The young leave the nest after 4–6 weeks.

Regent Parrot ♦ Regent Parakeet, Rock Pebbler Parakeet ♦
Polytelis anthopeplus

Description Length 15½in (40cm). Weight 5–7oz (150–200g). A long, narrow tail, long pointed wings, and tiny bill. The male has a greenish-yellow head and yellow underparts. Wings dark olive green with a large yellow area and small red patch. Ends of wings and tail are bluish black. The female is olive yellow with tail feathers edged with pink on the underside.

Call Soft, twittering notes and a harsh, prolonged warbling.

Distribution Found in Southern Australia.

Habitat Flooded eucalyptus woodland and adjacent arid scrublands, also other types of forests, and partially cleared land. They often travel considerable distances to feeding grounds, searching for grass seeds on the ground or feeding in the foliage of eucalyptus and acacias.

Food Seeds, nuts, fruits, flowers, nectar, and leaf buds. They also often raid wheat fields and orchards.

Breeding Nests are built in hollows of trees. 4–6 eggs may be laid up to 12ft (4m) down and incubated for 20 days. Chicks stay in the nest for about 4 weeks.

Ringnecked Parrot ♦ Port Lincoln Parrot, Port Lincoln Ringneck ♦
Barnardius zonarius

Medium-sized parrot with long graduated tail, closely related to the rosellas. One subspecies, restricted to south-western Australia is called Twenty-eight Parrot after its call which sounds like that number.
Description Length 15in (38cm). Weight 1½–6oz (120–170g). The head is black with a violet-blue throat, and yellow collar on the nape. The upperparts including back, wings and rump, breast and upper chest are green. The undersides are yellow, with greenish feathers near tail. Most of the tail feathers are pale blue with white tips, but the central tail feathers are blue green. The flight feathers are black, and the underside of the wings light blue. The bill is gray, the eye brown, and the legs gray. Sexes are similar but females have a brownish head. Immatures are similar to adults but duller.

Call A high pitched, shrill *kwink* repeated rapidly. One subspecies gives a three syllable call *twenty-eight*.
Distribution Ringnecked Parrots are found in central and western Australia.
Habitat These parrots are found in various types of habitat from the arid interior scrubland to coastal forest.
Food Their diet consists of seeds, grasses, herbaceous plants, fruits, especially eucalyptus, and nectar.
Breeding The male displays by crouching in front of the female moving his spread-tail from side to side, vibrating his closed wings. The female lays 4–7 eggs in a hollow branch, or hole in a tree, and does all the incubating. They hatch after 20 days, and the young fledge after 4 weeks. In some years there is a second brood.

Crimson Rosella ♦ Blue-cheeked Rosella (Crimson-winged Rosella, Pennant's Parakeet) ♦ *Platycercus elegans*

The Rosellas are usually brightly colored with well defined cheek patches and mottled backs. This species is popular in captivity and readily bred outside Australia.
Description Length 14in (36cm). Weight 5oz (145g). General color is bright crimson, with violet-blue cheeks, wings, and tail. The feathers of the back are crimson with bold black centers. The eye is dark brown, the bill gray brown, and the legs are gray. Sexes are similar, but there are several races which vary considerably in their amount of red. Some races are almost entirely yellow. The red coloration on immatures is limited to parts of the head and undertail covert, the majority of the plumage is dull green.
Call Low pitched *kweek* given in flight. Also heard is soft chattering when feeding, and shrill screeches given in alarm.

Distribution Eastern Australia. Introduced to New Zealand.
Habitat Coastal and montane forests up to 6,200ft (1,900m). Occurs in some suburbs, and can be abundant.
Food Mainly seeds, blossoms, and fruits; but insect larvae are also eaten.
Breeding Males display by crouching in front of females. 4–8 eggs are laid which hatch after 20 days. The young leave the nest after 4 weeks.

Red-fronted Parakeet ♦ Red-fronted Kakariki ♦
Cyanoramphus novaezelandiae

Several closely related parrots, previously considered to be subspecies or races of this bird are now extremely rare. **Description** Length 11in (28cm). Weight 2–4oz (50–110g). A small but relatively stocky parrot with almost totally green plumage, lighter on underside.

The leading edge of the flight feathers is blue. The rump, crown, and a stripe through the eye are crimson red. The eye is red, the bill bluish gray with darker tip. Sexes are similar, but males are larger than females. Immature birds have shorter tails and less red on head.
Call In flight or alarm call is strong *kek* repeated rapidly.
Distribution New Zealand
Habitat Can adapt to a variety of habitats from forest, to scrub and open areas. Island populations are totally terrestrial.
Food There is a strong seasonal variation in diet which includes seeds, fruit, nuts, berries, blossom, leaves, buds, and shoots.
Breeding 4–9 eggs are incubated for 19 days in a tree hole, bank, rock crevice or tussock grass. Young leave at 4–6 weeks.

Red-rumped Parrot ♦ Red-backed Parrot, Red-rumped Parakeet ♦
Psephotus haematonotus

These parrots spend much of their time feeding on the ground, scurrying unconcerned in front of observers.
Description Length 10½in (27cm). Weight 2–2½oz (55–70g). A generally bright green parrot with a small bill and a long graduated tail. The general plumage consists of green upperparts with lighter green breast, yellow underparts, and a red rump. The tail feathers are blue tipped white, except for the central feathers which are blue green. The female is much duller and is almost wholly olive green. The bill is black, the eye dark brown, legs gray. Immatures are duller.
Call Shrill disyllabic whistle emitted several times.

Distribution South-east Australia.
Habitat Similar to Blue Bonnet, but never far from water. Often found around towns and farms.
Food Feeds on grass, herbaceous plant seeds, and green vegetation.
Breeding 4–7 eggs are laid in hollow trees near water. The female incubates for 19 days. Fledging occurs by 4 weeks.

Pale-headed Rosella ♦ Blue-cheeked Rosella ♦ *Platycercus adscitus*

Common in captivity in Europe.
Description Length 12in (30cm). Weight 4–5oz (110–130g). The head, upperparts, and chest are pale yellow. The cheeks, lower breast, and abdomen are blue. Tail and flight feathers are similar to Crimson Rosella, and the undertail is red at the base. The feathers of the back are black with broad pale-yellow edging. The bill is horn-colored, the eye brown and the legs gray. Sexes similar. Immatures are similar to adults but duller, often with red markings on head.
Call Similar to Crimson Rosella but higher pitched, ascending notes.
Distribution North-east Australia.
Habitat Lowland forest, especially where woodland meets open areas. Abundant on some farmland, and at times considered a pest on crops.
Food They feed mainly on fruit, seeds, and blossoms.
Breeding Courtship takes place after heavy rains. 3–9 eggs are incubated for 20 days. Young leave the nest after 4 weeks.

Blue Bonnet ♦ *Psephotus haematogaster*

Small flocks are often found on the ground, feeding in the shade. They usually roost quietly during the hottest part of the day.
Description Length 11½in (29cm). Weight 3–4oz (75–105g). Upperparts, breast, parts of head olive brown. Crown and cheeks mauve blue, but lighter on cheeks. Underside mainly yellow with large red patch on lower belly. Flight feathers and tail largely blue. There are four races which show variations of red and yellow on the belly and underside of tail base. Some show a red bar across the shoulder. Females and immatures lack the blue crown and forehead.
Call A harsh *cluck-cluck* repeated regularly or in rapid succession. Also a piping whistle or fluty notes.
Distribution Interior of south and south-east Australia.
Habitat Grasslands with low densities of trees, arid scrubland, and riverine trees.
Food A diet of grass seeds, fruit, berries, blossom, nectar.
Breeding The incubation of the 4–9 eggs is carried out by the female only, over 17–19 days. Young fledge at 4 weeks.

Bourke's Parrot ♦ Bourke's Parakeet ♦ *Neophema bourkii*

A nomadic parrot which may suddenly appear or disappear from an area after several years.

Description Length 7½in (19cm). Weight 1½–2oz (40–50g). A small, mottled parrot which can be well camouflaged. Many of the feathers have dark centers and broad pale edging. Upperparts are mainly light brown and dusky white. The underside is paler with a distinct pinkish tinge. The sides, undertail base and rump are blue, as are the edges of the flight feathers. The tail feathers are bluish with white tips. The forehead is blue in males. The bill is gray, the eye brown, and the legs gray brown.

Call Soft whistle continually given when perched. Flight call is a soft *chewee*.

Distribution Found in interior of south and central Australia.

Habitat Arid acacia scrub.

Food They eat grass seeds and shoots, as well as herbaceous plant seeds.

Breeding Male displays by bowing and stretching in front of the female. 4 eggs are laid, hatching occurs after 18 days and young leave the nest 30 days later.

Rock Parrot ♦ Rock Parakeet ♦ *Neophema petrophila*

Description Length 8½in (22cm). Weight ¾–2oz (50–550g). Grass-green above and green-yellow to yellow below. The flight and tail feathers are blue, also a blue forehead which is bordered by pale blue line. The bill is gray brown, eyes brown, and legs gray. Females are similar but duller with no pale blue border to blue forehead. Immatures have no blue on the forehead.

Call Easily heard *tsit-tsit* repeated often. The second syllable usually slightly longer.

Distribution Found in south and south-west Australia.

Habitat Rarely found far inland, preferring coastal dunes and rocky areas.

Food Their diet consists of grass seeds and the seeds and fruits of other coastal plants.

Breeding The male courts the female by bobbing his head rapidly and offers food. 4–5 eggs are laid in a rocky crevice and incubated by the female for 18 days. Fledging occurs after 4 weeks.

Swift Parrot ◆ *Lathamus discolor*

The clearing of eucalyptus forest in its range, and some pressure from trapping has resulted in this parrot's decline.
Description Length 10in (25cm). Weight 2–3oz (50–75g). A largely green parrot with a long pointed tail. The undertail and underwings are red. The tail is dark red. The forehead and throat are bright red, partly bordered by a yellow line in front of the eye. It has a blue crown. The leading edge of the flight feathers are blue, and the shoulder is red. The eye is orange yellow, the bill pale horn-colored. The legs are brown. Sexes are similar. Immatures are duller with less red on throat, and a brown eye.
Call The *clink* sound is repeated very rapidly in succession.

Distribution South-east Australia.
Habitat Woodland, parkland, towns.
Food They feed mainly on pollen and nectar, but they also eat insect larvae, fruits, berries, and vegetation.
Breeding These parrots are migratory, breeding only in Tasmania, but return to the mainland when breeding has finished. They nest gregariously, laying 3–6 eggs which are incubated for 20 days apparently by the female only. The young are ready to leave the nest at 6 weeks.

Greater Vasa Parrot ♦ Vasa Parrot ♦ *Coracopsis vasa*

Description Length 20in (50cm). Weight 17oz (480g). A large, chunky parrot, with a heavy, broad bill and a long, rounded tail. Entirely sooty black except for pinkish bare skin around the brown eye. Bill pale gray. Sexes are similar. Immature birds' plumage is more brown black.
Call Noisy birds, their harsh *kraar*, and drawn-out, descending *pee-aw* easily heard.
Distribution Madagascar and Comoro Islands.
Habitat Lowland forest and up to 3,300 ft (1,000m). Also found on coastal plains.
Food Their diet consists of seeds, fruit, nuts, and berries.

Breeding In breeding condition skin becomes yellow around face, on crown in female, and may be visible beneath lower mandible on male. Both sexes have unusually large external sex organs. 3–4 eggs are laid in a deep arboreal nest chamber, and incubated for 17 days. The young leave the nest after 7 weeks.

Gray Parrot ♦ *Psittacus erithacus*

This parrot is a popular domestic pet in western countries, mainly because it is a very lovable and intelligent bird, and an excellent mimic of human speech. In the wild however it is shy and wary.

Description Length 13in (33cm). Weight 14oz (405g). The general plumage is gray, the tail feathers only are red. The face is whitish, the rump a pale gray and the wing-tips black. The bill is black and the legs are dark-gray in color. The eyes are pale yellow. Sexes are similar.

Call A melodic whistle as well as a series of high-pitched screeches. This parrot is also an accomplished mimic and can copy all sorts of sounds including human speech.

Distribution West coast and Central Africa up to Kenya and Tanzania.

Habitat Mainly found in lowland forests, but also sometimes in savannah woodlands, open country, and mangrove swamps. They are common birds in their range, particularly around towns and villages. Usually found in pairs or small family groups, at dusk they may congregate in large flocks of several hundred in a single tall tree.

Food Seeds, nuts, fruits, and berries, particularly the fruits of the oil palm. Also known to raid maize fields.

Breeding They nest in the holes of old trees and lay 3–4 eggs. The female alone incubates the eggs, but the male helps to feed the chicks once they hatch. The young leave the nest after about 10 weeks.

Blue-crowned Hanging-Parrot ♦ *Loriculus galgulus*

Hanging parrots are tiny birds with very short tails. Their name is derived from their habit of roosting upside-down. They are closely related to lovebirds and females also carry nest materials in their body feathers.
Description Length 4¾in (12cm). Weight 1oz (24g). A very small, green parrot with a scarlet rump, red throat and upper breast, golden mantle and a blue crown. The female has an all green throat and less blue on crown. The iris is dark brown, the bill black, and the legs light brown. Immatures are

more or less all dull green except for the rump, and have a brownish bill.
Call Very high-pitched short buzz *dzee* given in flight.
Distribution Found in Malaysia, Sumatra, Borneo, Singapore.
Habitat Fairly common in lowland forest and wooded areas up to 1,640ft (500m).
Food Nectar, fruit, seeds, and blossoms.
Breeding Small enough to nest in large bamboo. 3–4 eggs are laid, and hatch after 20 days. Young leave the nest after 4 weeks.

Senegal Parrot ♦ *Poicephalus senegalus*

Usually found in groups of up to 20, but these are shy birds and difficult to approach.
Description Length 9in (23cm). Weight 4½–5½oz (125–155g). A stocky parrot with a short tail and relatively large head and bill. The head is entirely dark gray, the upperparts, chest, and thighs are green, being brighter below. The rest of the underparts, underwing, and rump are yellow. The bill is gray, the eye yellow, and the legs brown. Immatures are duller with a brownish head and brown eye.
Call A variety of screeches and whistles.
Distribution Western-central Africa.
Habitat Open woodland, savannah, and wooded farmland.
Food Seeds, grain, fruit, and leaf buds.

Breeding 3–4 eggs are incubated for 27 days by both sexes. The young fledge after 10 weeks.

Meyer's Parrot ♦ Brown Parrot ♦ *Poicephalus meyeri*

Description Length 8½in (22cm). Weight 3½–4½oz (100–135g). The head, breast, and upperparts are brown gray, while the underparts and rump are blue-green. There is yellow under the wing and the thighs are yellow. There is a yellow patch on bend of wing and a variable band on the crown. The bill is dark gray, the eye orange red, and the legs gray. Immatures are greenish brown above and greener below. Yellow patches are smaller or absent.
Call High pitched *chee* repeated three times, or harsh *kraw-er*. Mated pairs will also duet *klink-klink..cheewee..cheewee*. Also a variety of alarm notes.
Distribution Found in central, east and southern Africa.
Habitat A wide variety of wooded habitat from savannah to acacia scrub.
Food Seeds, nuts, berries, fruit.
Breeding 3–4 eggs are laid. Incubation lasts 26 days. The young leave the nest after 9 weeks.

Rosy-faced Lovebird ♦ Peach-faced Lovebird ♦ *Agapornis roseicollis*

Lovebirds are so called because of their habit of mutual preening. They are small, stocky parrots with short tails and are very popular as cage birds.

Description Length 6in (15cm). Weight 1½–2½ oz (45–65g). Mostly green, lighter below, with face, forehead, throat, and breast red to rose-pink. The rump is blue, and the undersides of the wings and tail are also bluish. The eye is dark brown, surrounded by a narrow white eye-ring. The legs are gray, and the bill is pale horn-colored with greenish cutting edges. Sexes are similar, but immatures are duller with a brownish forehead and darker bill.

Call Metallic shriek repeated several times, getting more rapid when alarmed.

Distribution South-west Africa.

Habitat Found in open habitats from lowland up to 5,250ft (1,600m) near drinking water.

Food Seeds, buds, and flowers are the main constituents in their diet.

Breeding They nest communally in crevices or in old weaver-bird nests. The female gathers nest material by tucking small items into body feathers. 4–6 eggs are laid and incubated for 23 days. The young leave after 6 weeks.

Masked Lovebird ♦ Yellow-collared Lovebird ♦ *Agapornis personata*

Description Length 6in (15cm). Weight 1½–2oz (45–50g). The upperparts are generally green, with green yellow underside turning to yellow on the breast and neck forming a distinct collar. The head and throat are dark brown. The bill is red and the eye dark brown surrounded by a wide area of white bare skin.

Call Hitch-pitched chattering.
Distribution Tanzania, Kenya.
Habitat Wooded bushland between 3,600–5,900ft (1,100–1,800m).
Food Seeds, buds, and flowers.
Breeding Colonially in tree holes and even in buildings. 4–8 eggs are laid, and incubated for 23 days. Young fledge after 6 weeks.

Rose-ringed Parakeet ♦ Ring-necked Parakeet ♦ *Psittacula krameri*

This is the most widely distributed of all parrots. In addition to its natural range, it has been introduced to many countries world-wide.

Description Length 15½in (39cm). Weight 4–5oz (105–140g). A medium-sized parrot with a very long, narrow, pointed tail. Mostly light green with a yellowish undertail. The chin is black spreading across as a broad stripe along lower cheeks, this joins a narrow, rose pink collar which encircles the lower neck. There is a bluish tinge on the back of the neck. The eye is orange yellow and the bill red with a black base. Different subspecies have varying amounts of red and black on the bill. Females lack black chin, rose collar, and the bluish tinge on the nape. They also have shorter central tail feathers. Immatures are similar to females but have a pink bill and gray eye.

Call Harsh, shrill scream *kee-ak* given frequently in flight.

Distribution Africa, parts of Middle East, India, China, and introduced to other countries including Europe and USA.

Habitat Open forest and cultivated land.

Food Seeds, fruit, berries, blossoms, and nectar. They are considered a serious pest in some orchards.

Breeding An elaborate courtship involves the female spreading her wings slightly, and rubbing her bill against the male's before accepting regurgitated food. The nest is made in a hollow tree, where 4–6 eggs are incubated by the female for 24 days. The young fledge after 7 weeks.

Plum-headed Parakeet ◆ *Psittacula cyanocephala*

Description Length 13in (33cm). Weight 2½–3oz (65–90g). Mainly green with purple-red head bordered by black neck collar and chin. Long central tail feathers blue with white tips, rest of tail yellow green with yellow tips. Underwing and rump greenish blue. Dark red patch on wing coverts. Eye yellow white, upper mandible orange yellow, lower mandible black. Female has dull blue-gray head, yellow neck collar and no red patch on wing. Immature has shorter tail and mainly green head.
Call Flight call is a shrill *tooi*.
Distribution Sri Lanka, Indian sub-continent north to Nepal and Pakistan.
Habitat Open woodland around foothills up to 4,900ft (1,500m).
Food Seeds, fruit, nuts, and blossom.

Breeding Nests in tree holes, may use old woodpecker nests. 4–6 eggs are brooded by the female. They hatch after 24 days and fledge after 7 weeks.

Blue-and-yellow Macaw ♦ Blue-and-gold Macaw ♦ *Ara ararauna*

This is one of the most familiar parrots in captivity, but looks truly spectacular when seen in flight over the forest canopy. Macaws of this genus are easily identified by their bare facial skin.

Description Length 33½in (85cm). Weight 35–45oz (1,000–1,280g). A large macaw with bright blue upperparts and a green forehead. Underparts, including underwing and undertail, are bright orange yellow. The upper throat is black, bordering bare, white facial skin with narrow lines of black feathers. The massive bill is gray black, the eye is yellow, and the legs dark gray.

Call Flight call very loud, harsh *raak*.

Distribution Northern South America.

Habitat Relatively common in gallery forest and humid lowland forest near water.

Food Seeds, fruits, nuts.

Breeding 2–4 eggs are laid in a dead palm trunk. Incubation lasts 24 days, and the young birds fledge after 13–14 weeks.

Hyacinth Macaw ◆ *Anodorhynchus hyacinthinus*

Macaws are mostly large birds with long, pointed tails. Among them are the largest and arguably the most spectacular parrots. This macaw's beauty and desirability has been its downfall. Trapping and a naturally slow maturity have resulted in its current low population.
Description Length 39in (100cm). Weight 42–52oz (1,200–1,450g). The largest parrot, almost wholly deep cobalt blue, with darker flight feathers and contrasting bright yellow, bare skin around eye and lower mandible.

The huge gray-black bill is the most powerful of any bird.
Call Alarm call is harsh shriek.
Distribution Brazil, Bolivia, and Paraguay.
Habitat These birds inhabit riverine forest in semi-open grassland.
Food Fruits, nuts, and seeds.
Breeding Usually 2 eggs are laid in hollow trees, often palms. The female incubates for 28 days, and the young fledge at 14 weeks.

Scarlet Macaw ♦ *Ara macao*

Description Length 35in (88cm). Weight 35–40oz (900–1,120g). The general body plumage and tail are bright scarlet red. The flight feathers, rump and base of the undertail are blue. The folded wing shows a large yellow patch (this is green in the similar Red-and-Green Macaw). Bare whitish facial skin has no or inconspicuous feather lines. The upper mandible is mostly whitish horn with a black lower mandible. The eye is yellow and the legs are gray. Immatures have a shorter tail.

Call Harsh coarse drawn out *raaaagh*. Louder and more aggressive in voice than Blue-and-yellow Macaw.

Distribution Northern South America and Central America.

Habitat Gallery and lowland forest, particularly along rivers.

Food Seeds, fruits, nuts, and berries.

Breeding Nests high up in cavities in large trees. 2–4 eggs are incubated for 24 days. Young fledge after 15 weeks.

Sun Conure ◆ Sun Parakeet ◆ *Aratinga solstitialis*

Description Length 12in (30cm). Weight 4oz (120g). A stunning parrot, the body and both upper and underwing coverts are yellow with a varying orange wash. The wings and tail are green with some blue tinge to the flight feather tips and the tail. The bill is gray, the eye brown, and the feet are gray. Sexes are similar. Immatures are variable but generally have a greenish plumage with less yellow.

Call Very noisy birds often heard before seen. Flight call is a disyllabic screech.
Distribution Venezuela, Brazil, Guianas.
Habitat Scrubland and savannah.
Food Seeds, fruit, and nuts.
Breeding 3–4 eggs are laid and incubated for 24 days, with fledging occurring between 7–8 weeks.

Nanday Conure ♦ *Nandayas nenday*

Large flocks of these conures travel widely over the South American lowlands during the non-breeding season.

Description
Length 12½in (31cm). Weight 5oz (140g). A mainly green parrot with dark greenish-blue flight feathers and a pointed tail. The underside is lighter yellowish green with light blue on the breast. The cap and upper throat around the bill are black. The eye is dark brown surrounded by pale whitish bare skin, the bill is also black. The legs are pink brown with red thighs. Immatures have less blue on the chest and shorter tails.

Call A rather loud voice makes them less popular as pets. The flight call is a loud screech *kreeaw*.

Distribution Bolivia, Brazil, Paraguay, and Argentina. Feral populations in USA.

Habitat Common in seasonally flooded open grassland.

Food The diet is made up of seeds, fruit, nuts, and berries.

Breeding There is little information from the wild. Females lay 3–5 eggs and incubate for 24 days. Young leave the nest after 8 weeks.

Thick-billed Parrot ♦ *Rhynchopsitta pachyrhyncha*

A nomadic parrot which moves in response to the abundance of pine cones. It is now threatened with habitat degradation throughout its limited range.

Description Length 15in (38cm). Weight 11oz (300g). Quite a large, stocky parrot, mostly green in color with a short but pointed tail. The forehead, above the eye, thigh, and bend of the wing are red.

The underwing has a bright yellow patch visible in flight. The iris is yellow, the bill black, and the legs gray. Immatures lack the red above the eye, and on the bend of the wing, and have a light horn colored bill.

Call Loud raucous screech.

Distribution Mexico, formerly resident in Arizona, USA.

Habitat Highland pine forest.

Food Mainly pine seeds.

Breeding 2–4 eggs are laid, usually in dead pine trees. The female incubates for 27 days, and the young fledge after 8–9 weeks.

Patagonian Conure ♦ Burrowing Parakeet ♦ *Cyanoliseus patagonus*

These communal parrots are migratory, moving with season food abundance. **Description** Length 20in (50cm). Weight 8–14oz (240–390g). A large parrot with a long graduated tail. The head, upperparts, and wings are olive brown, becoming gray brown on chest and lower breast. Has variable pale gray marks on the sides of the chest. The lower abdomen, rump, and undertail area are yellow, with a red belly and thighs. The flight feathers are greenish blue, with an olive-green tail. The bill is gray, the eyes are pale yellow with white bare skin and the legs are flesh color. Immatures have a whitish upper mandible.

Call A shrill screech in flight.
Distribution Chile, Argentina, Uruguay.
Habitat Open country often near streams.
Food Seeds, fruits, and berries.
Breeding These parrots nest communally in holes in sandstone cliff faces and river banks, which they excavate themselves. The burrows up to 9ft (3m) in length. The female incubates 2–4 eggs for 24 days. The young remain in the nest for 7–9 weeks.

Painted Parakeet ◆ Painted Conure ◆ *Pyrrhura picta*

Description Length 8½in (22cm). Weight 2oz (55g). Generally has a green plumage with blue flight feathers and a red patch on the bend of the wing. The tail, rump, and belly are dull red. The neck, throat, and breast feathers are dark brown with marked, broad whitish edges giving a distinctive scalloped look. Ear patches are invariably white, but the rest of the head color varies with subspecies, usually a mix of dull blue, brown, and dull red (all bright red in the Brazilian form). Immatures are like adults but have very little red.

Call Descending harsh, scream *ee-ee-m* given in flight. Also harsh *eek*.
Distribution Found in Northern South America through Amazon basin, also Venezuela and Guianas.
Habitat Humid forest and borders up to 6,550ft (2,000m).
Food Seeds, fruit, nuts, berries, blossoms, and vegetation.
Breeding 4–8 eggs are incubated for 23 days. The young birds fledge at 6–7 weeks.

Slender-billed Parakeet ♦ Slender-billed Conure ♦
Enicognathus leptorhynchus

Description Length 16in (40cm). Weight 9oz (240g). Largely dull green feathers with darker tips. The tail is brown red with brighter red around eye and forehead. The oddly long and thin, black bill is used to extract seeds from spiky traucaria cones. The eyes are orange red and the feet are brown. Sexes and immatures are similar.
Call Constant screeching in flight or alarmed. Shrill chattering when feeding.
Distribution Chile.

Habitat Mainly lowland forest but also open country during winter.
Food Their diet consists of seeds, fruit, berries, nuts, buds, and roots.
Breeding 2–6 eggs are laid in a tree hollow and then incubated for 26 days, mainly by the female. The young birds stay in the nest for 7 weeks.

Spectacled Parrotlet ♦ *Forpus conspicillatus*

These parrotlets are small green parrots with short wedge-shaped tails.
Description Length 5in (12cm). Weight 1oz (30g). Almost totally green, paler and more yellow below. Blue rump, wings, and around the eye. Bill a pale gray, the eye brown and the legs pale brown. The female lacks any blue color and is very difficult to distinguish from many other closely related species. Female immatures are like the adult. Immature males have blue replaced by bright green tinged with yellow or blue.

Call Constant finch-like chattering.
Distribution Found in Venezuela, Colombia, Panama.
Habitat Dry open woodland and secondary forest.
Food Grass seeds, berries, and fruit.
Breeding The nest cavity is often relatively low down in any wood. 4–6 eggs are incubated for a period of 18 days. Fledging occurs at 4 weeks.

Monk Parakeet ♦ Quaker Parakeet ♦ *Myiopsitta monachus*

Highly gregarious parrots which move around in flocks of up to a hundred or more. They nest communally.
Description Length 12½in (31cm). Weight 5oz (150g). A medium-sized parrot with a long, graduated tail, green upperparts and tail, blue flight feathers. Crown and forehead are gray, throat whitish becoming gray on breast with paler edges giving a barred appearance. The abdomen is yellow with a green tinge. The eye is brown, the bill pale horn, and the legs gray. Immatures have greenish foreheads.
Call Loud, staccato shriek in flight. High-pitched chattering when feeding.
Distribution Bolivia, Brazil, Argentina. Established in USA.
Habitat Found commonly in a variety of drier lowland wooded or open areas.
Food Seeds, fruit, berries, nuts, buds, blossoms, insect larvae.
Breeding Unique among parrots, builds huge communal nests with thorny twigs, in the tops of trees. The female lays 5–6 eggs and incubates for 24 days. The young fledge at 6–7 weeks.

Mountain Parakeet ♦ *Bolborhynchus aurifrons*

Conspicuous but poorly known parrots found in the high Andes.
Description Length 6in (18cm). Weight 2oz (45g). Quite a plain parrot with entirely green upperparts apart from dark-bluish flight feathers. The cheeks are bright emerald green, and the remainder of the underparts yellow being brighter nearer the head and extending to the forehead. The small bill is pale horn, the eyes are brown and the legs pink brown. Females are generally darker with less yellow on face, and a green forehead. Immatures are similar to females but have shorter tails.
Call Loud screaming calls are given in flight.
Distribution Found in Peru, Bolivia, Chile, and Argentina.
Habitat As the name suggests they are found at high altitudes up to 13,000ft (4,000m) in open shrubby areas.
Food Seeds, fruit, and berries.
Breeding The female lays 4–5 eggs. These are then incubated for 23 days, the young fledging at 7 weeks.

Canary-winged Parakeet ♦ *Brotogeris versicolurus*

An abundant parrot often seen in small flocks but can form large noisy roosts.
Description Length 8½in (22cm). Weight 2½oz (70g). A small parrot with a longish, pointed tail and overall dull green. The outer wings are dark blue contrasting conspicuously with the inner wing which is white and yellow. The bill is pale horn, the eye brown, and the legs grayish pink. Immatures have less white in the wings, and many of the feathers have green tips.

Call Series of shrill metallic *screek* notes.
Distribution Interior and eastern South America. Feral population in USA.
Habitat Lowland forest to open, lightly wooded grassland.
Food Seeds, fruit, berries, and blossoms.
Breeding 3–6 eggs are incubated for 26 days. The young are in the nest for 7 weeks.

Black-headed Parrot ◆ Black-capped Caique, Black-headed Caique ◆ *Pionites melanocephala*

The Black-headed parrot flies in small flocks just above the forest canopy.
Description Length 9in (23cm). Weight 4½–6oz (130–170g). These parrots have a distinctive plumage, with green wings and upperparts. The underparts are white with yellow undertail, throat, and neck which contrasts with a black cap. The eye is red with green feathers below, the bill is gray black and the legs gray. Sexes are similar, but immatures can be distinguished by pale plumage and pale bill.
Call High-pitched distinctive screech *cleeooo* in flight. Otherwise, a variety of unmusical and piping notes.

Distribution South America north of the Amazon.
Habitat Fairly common in lowland forest.
Food A diet of fruit, berries, and seeds.
Breeding 3 eggs are incubated for 26 days. Fledging occurs after 10 weeks.

Blue-headed Parrot ◆ *Pionus menstruus*

This bird is one of the commonest neotropical parrots.
Description Length 11in (27cm). Weight 9oz (250g). A broad winged and short tailed parrot with mostly green plumage. The base of the tail is red, and the head, nape, and breast are blue. The bill is gray with pink-red base, the eye is brown, and the legs gray.

Call Noisy, uttering a variety of screeches and screaming notes. A harsh, high-pitched *keewenk*, *keewenk* uttered in flight.
Distribution Found in Brazil, Bolivia, Colombia north to Costa Rica, Trinidad.
Habitat Humid lowland forest, and secondary partly cleared areas.
Food Fruit, seeds, nuts, berries, blossoms, and buds.
Breeding 3–4 eggs are incubated for 26 days. The young birds fledge after about 10 weeks.

St. Vincent Amazon ♦ St. Vincent Parrot ♦ *Amazona guildingii*

This parrot has, until recently, suffered from habitat loss and over trapping.
Description Length 16in (40cm). Weight 20oz (580g). There are two main color morphs, one green, and one yellow brown, but many birds are intermediate, and few individuals look the same. Birds of the yellow morph have creamy white forehead and crown, merging to orange head. The cheeks are blue, and the upper neck feathers olive green edged black. Underparts are bronze brown with blackish feather edges. The wings are bronze, with black flight feathers, orange or green bases and a blue-tinge. Undersides of wings and tail are yellow. The tail is violet blue with broad yellow tip and orange base. The bill is horn colored, the eye orange, and the legs are pale gray. Green morph differs with upperparts mainly dusky green. Immatures are similar but much duller, particularly on the head.
Call Flight call is a loud *cor, cor*, and a loud squeak-like noise is made when feeding.
Distribution Found only on the island of St. Vincent in the Caribbean.
Habitat Montane forest.
Food A diet consisting of fruits, seeds, nuts, berries, and flowers.
Breeding 2 eggs are incubated for 25 days in the hollow of large trees. The young remain in the nest for up to 10 weeks.

Yellow-crowned Amazon ♦ Yellow-headed Amazon, Yellow-fronted Amazon ♦ *Amazona ochrocephala*

Familiar in captivity, around nine distinct subspecies are recognized. These are distinguished by geographic distribution and head coloration.

Description Length 14in (35cm). Weight 13–18oz (380–500g). General plumage is green with varying amounts of yellow on the head. Some subspecies have yellow restricted to a small area on back of the neck or forecrown, others have an entirely yellow head. The bend of the wing is often red with some yellow along the edge. Flight feathers are violet blue at wing tip, becoming green toward the body. There is also a red patch on the wing, conspicuous when opened. The bill is dark gray to pale yellow, and the eye is orange surrounded by whitish skin.

Immatures tend to be duller than the adults, many feathers have more pronounced blackish edging, and red and yellow coloring is less extensive. The bill is entirely dark gray and the iris is dark brown.

Call In captivity is a renowned mimic and talker, although can be noisy. In flight, call is a repeated yapping, and a variety of metallic shrieks and whistling notes.

Distribution Mexico south through central America to Amazonia including Brazil and Colombia. Feral populations in USA.

Habitat Humid forests, drier woodland, and wooded grasslands, even into cultivated and suburban areas.

Food A diet of fruits, nuts, berries, and blossoms.

Breeding Between 2–4 eggs are incubated by the female for 26 days. Young fledge after 9–11 weeks.

Red-fan Parrot ♦ Hawk-headed Parrot ♦ *Deroptyus accipitrinus*

This parrot has long, blue-edged feathers at the nape. During play, fear or aggression, these are raised to form a fan. Fairly common in small groups of up to 20.
Description Length 13in (33cm). Weight 7–10oz (190–280g). Similar in structure to Amazon parrots, but the feathers of the nape, hindneck, breast, and abdomen are dark red, broadly edged with blue. The forehead and crown are buff-white, and the rest of the head is dark brown with white streaks. The upperparts, thighs, flanks, undertail, and underwings are green. The wings and tail are brown black. The eyes are yellow, legs gray, and the bill gray black. Immatures lack the whitish crown, have duller underparts, gray brown eye, and have whitish lower mandible and skin surrounding the eye.

Call Main call is an abrupt, sharp note, followed by two prolonged notes. Very noisy with a wide variety of other calls including single bugle-like notes, chattering, soft piping whistles and a high-pitched *slit*.
Distribution Peru, Ecuador, Colombia, Venezuela, Brazil, Guianas.
Habitat Undisturbed lowland rainforest, but not seasonally flooded forest.
Food Fruits, seeds, nuts, and berries.
Breeding Nests in old woodpecker holes. 2–4 eggs are incubated for 26 days, and the young fledge after 9 weeks.

Red-crowned Amazon ♦ Green-cheeked Amazon, Green-cheeked Parrot ♦ *Amazona viridenalis*

Heavy exploitation for the captive trade and habitat loss have caused a drastic decline in this parrot's abundance over the last few decades. Previously they had occurred in large flocks that numbered up to a hundred.

Description Length 13in (33cm). Weight 10oz (270g). Like many Amazon parrots, mostly green in color. The body feathers have dark edges, especially on the neck giving a scaly appearance. The head has a red cap and a violet band down the side of the neck. The wings have dark tips, and a red patch on the upper side. The bill is pale yellowish, the eye is yellow and the legs pale gray. Females have less extensive red caps, and immatures can be distinguished by having red only on the forehead.

Call A loud scream *kreeo kraw kraw*.

Distribution Mexico, and feral in USA.

Habitat Found in evergreen forest and dry wooded ridges and canyons up to 4,000ft (1,200m).

Food Fruits, seeds, nuts, berries, buds, and flowers make up the majority of the diet. They have been considered a pest on crops in the past.

Breeding Courtship involves the males offering small food items to the female. She lays between 2–4 eggs and incubates for 28 days. Young fledge after 9 weeks.

Index